To my favorite teacher
and love of my life, Krista,
and our three "fruits" –
Kate, Brandan & Nathan

1-2-3-4 BANANA

WRITTEN BY MR BRAD

ILLUSTRATED BY SARAH LOWE

Are you ready to count?

First...
Start with one
hand out

...like this!

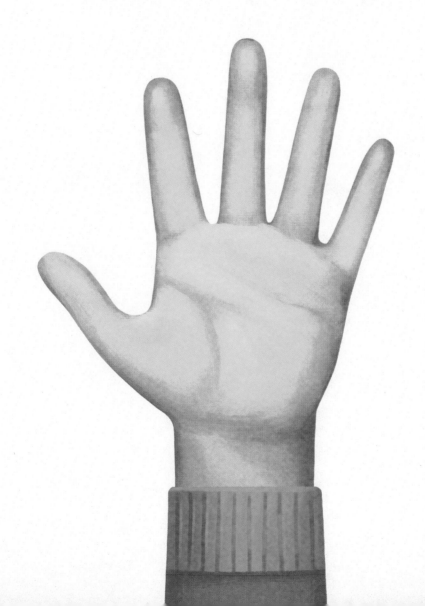

Let's GO!

1 2 3 4

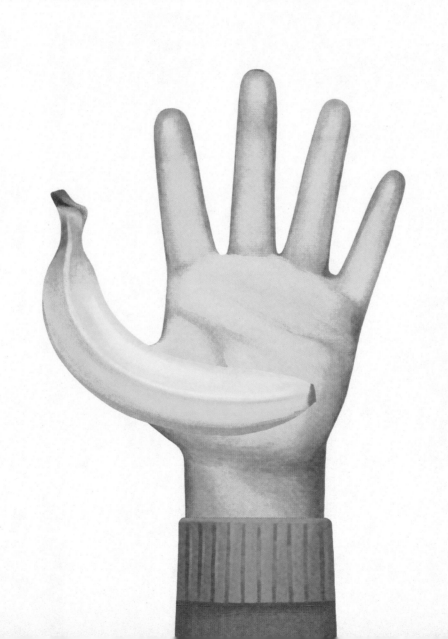

Banana!

Banana?
That's not right...

Let's try this again...

1 Banana 3

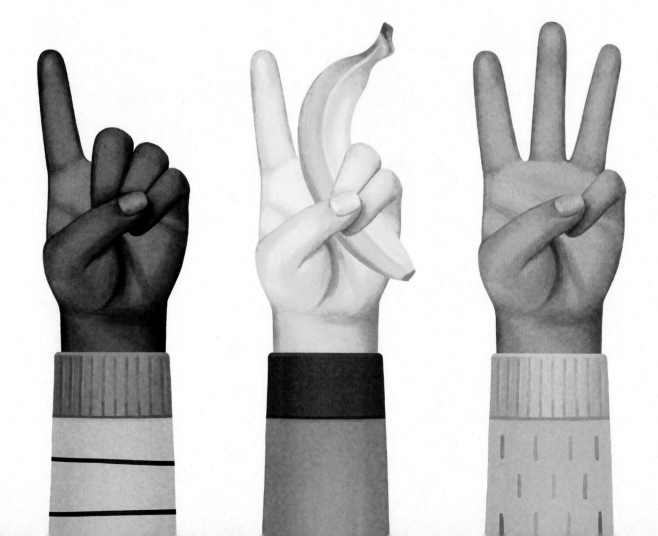

4   Banana

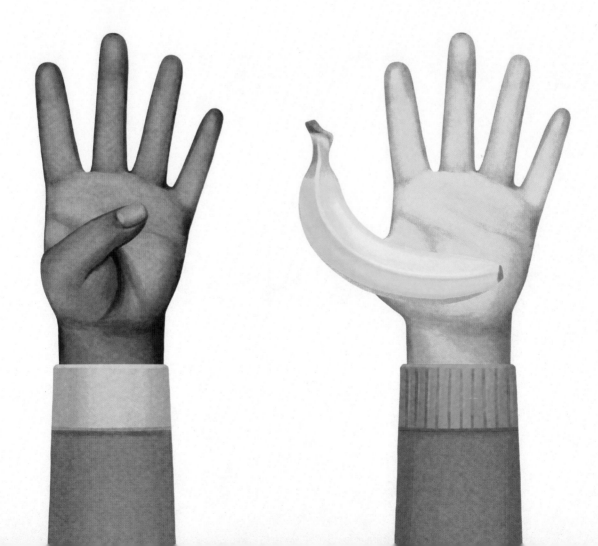

Wait...that's even worse!

Oh NO!!

I know we can
do this...

Let's try again...

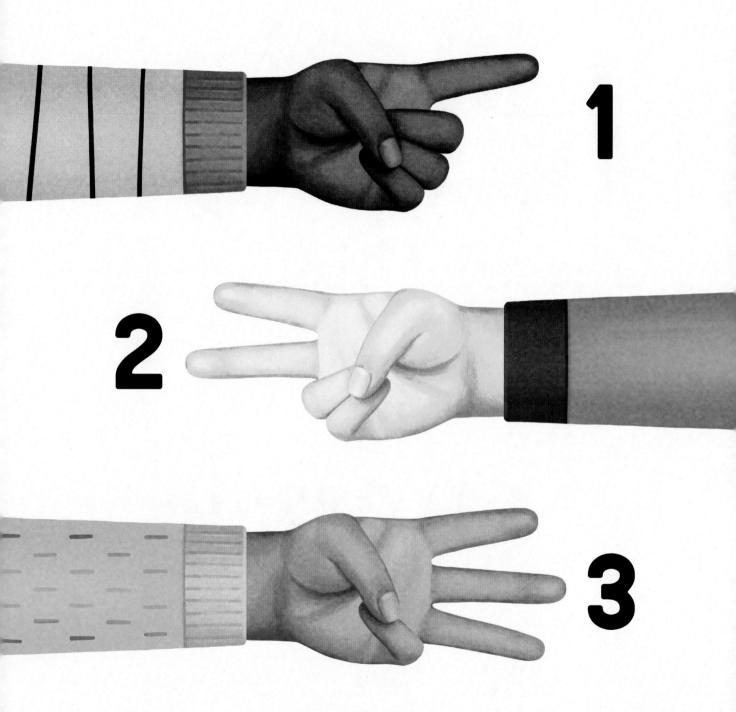

4

5

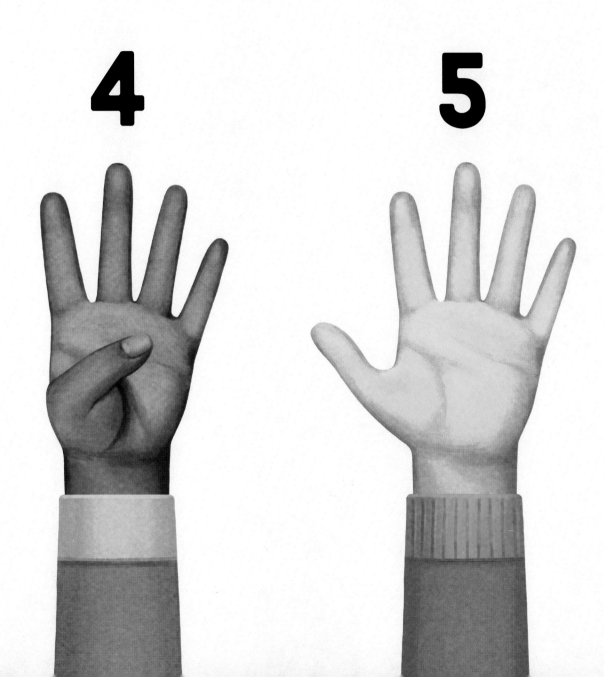

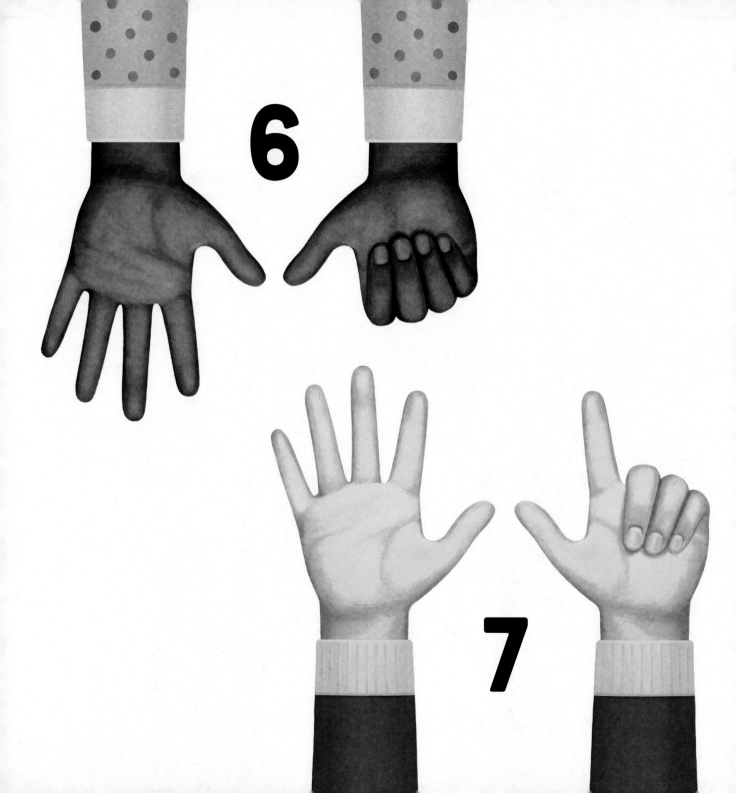

8

9

Banana!

Oh No!!!

We were SOOO close!

1 LAST TIME!!!

Can we do this?

YES!

6   7

8   9

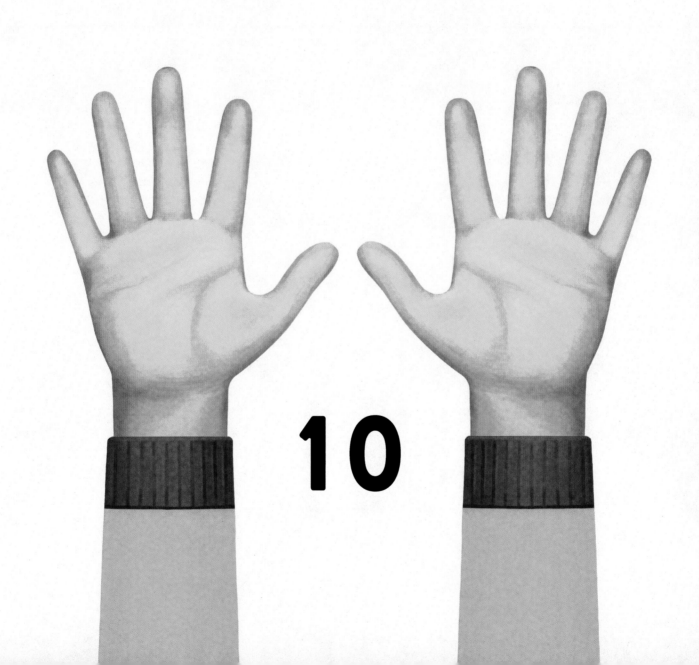

10

10!!!!

We did it!!!

Banana

Made in the USA
Monee, IL
13 September 2021

77953469R00021